the unsinkable charlie brown

Books by Charles M. Schulz

the unsinkable charlie brown

A NEW **PEANUTS** BOOK
BY CHARLES M. SCHULZ

HOLT, RINEHART AND WINSTON
New York • Chicago • San Francisco

First published in book form in 1967.

Library of Congress Catalog Card Number: 67-14271

Published, March, 1967
Sixth Printing, December, 1970

SBN: 03–064130–6

Printed in the United States of America

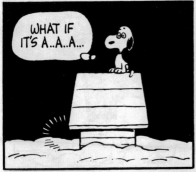

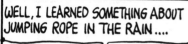
WELL, I LEARNED SOMETHING ABOUT JUMPING ROPE IN THE RAIN....

SOME JUMP ROPES **SHRINK**!

R R R R R R

THAT VACUUM CLEANER SURE MAKES A LOT OF NOISE...

R R R R R

R R R R R R R R R R

YOU'D MAKE A LOT OF NOISE TOO IF SOMEONE WERE PUSHING YOU ACROSS A CARPET ON YOUR FACE!

DEAR EDITOR OF "LETTERS TO THE EDITOR", HOW HAVE YOU BEEN?

"HOW HAVE YOU BEEN?" WHAT SORT OF LETTER IS THAT TO WRITE TO AN EDITOR?

I JUST THOUGHT HE MIGHT APPRECIATE HAVING SOMEONE INQUIRE ABOUT THE STATE OF HIS HEALTH

EDITORS ARE SORT OF HUMAN, TOO, YOU KNOW!

SCHULZ

DOES IT BOTHER YOU TO THINK THAT THERE MAY BE PEOPLE AROUND WHO DISLIKE YOU?

DISLIKE **ME**? HOW COULD ANYONE POSSIBLY DISLIKE **ME**? THERE'S NOTHING TO DISLIKE!

JEALOUS, MAYBE....YES, I COULD UNDERSTAND THAT...I CAN SEE HOW SOMEONE COULD BE JEALOUS OF ME...BUT DISLIKE? NO, THAT'S JUST NOT POSSIBLE...

SO GETTING BACK TO YOUR ORIGINAL QUESTION...

FORGET IT..

SCHULZ

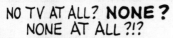

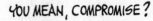

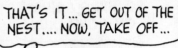

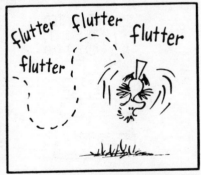

TRY TO STAY CALM.... I HAVE TERRIBLE NEWS!

DAD'S BEEN TRANSFERRED! WE'RE MOVING TO A NEW CITY!

AAUGH!

THIS MAY BE MY LAST GAME, CHARLIE BROWN

MY DAD'S BEEN TRANSFERRED... WE'RE MOVING TO A NEW CITY... I'LL PROBABLY NEVER SEE YOU AGAIN...

UNLESS, OF COURSE, WE HAPPEN TO GO TO THE SAME COLLEGE.. WHAT COLLEGE DO YOU THINK YOU'LL BE GOING TO?

IT'S KIND OF HARD TO DECIDE IN THE LAST HALF OF THE NINTH INNING

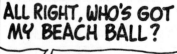

LET'S HUSTLE A LITTLE MORE ON THOSE FLY-BALLS!

C'MON! MOVE IN ON THOSE GROUNDERS! THROW THE BALL! DON'T HANG ON TO IT!

ALL RIGHT! EVERYBODY OVER HERE ON THE DOUBLE! LET'S GO!

OKAY, TEAM, THIS IS THE START OF A NEW SEASON, AND I HAVE A FEW WORDS TO SAY..

NOW, I THINK NO ONE WILL DENY THAT SPIRIT PLAYS AN IMPORTANT ROLE IN WINNING BALL GAMES..

SOME MIGHT SAY THAT IT PLAYS THE MOST IMPORTANT ROLE..

THE DESIRE TO WIN IS WHAT MAKES A TEAM GREAT..WINNING IS EVERYTHING!

THE ONLY THING THAT MATTERS IS TO COME IN FIRST PLACE!

WHAT I'M TRYING TO SAY IS THAT NO ONE EVER REMEMBERS WHO COMES IN SECOND PLACE!

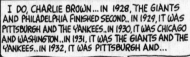

I DO, CHARLIE BROWN... IN 1928, THE GIANTS AND PHILADELPHIA FINISHED SECOND.. IN 1929, IT WAS PITTSBURGH AND THE YANKEES..IN 1930, IT WAS CHICAGO AND WASHINGTON..IN 1931, IT WAS THE GIANTS AND THE YANKEES..IN 1932, IT WAS PITTSBURGH AND...

AND ANOTHER GREAT SEASON GETS UNDERWAY!

I DON'T KNOW ABOUT THIS NEXT BATTER, CHARLIE BROWN..HE'S PRETTY GOOD..

THAT'S RIGHT, CHARLIE BROWN.. YOU'D BETTER WATCH HIM..

WELL, WHAT DO YOU THINK? SHALL I GIVE HIM THE OL' CHANGE OF PACE? THE LET-UP?

NO, HE'D KILL IT, CHARLIE BROWN...JUST GIVE HIM FAST ONES, BUT KEEP THEM LOW..

LINUS IS RIGHT, CHARLIE BROWN..

OKAY..FAST BALLS IT IS... LET'S GET 'IM!

Z

?
Z

Z

WHAT WOULD HE DO IF WE EVER STARTED PLAYING **NIGHT** GAMES?
Z

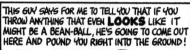

THIS GUY SAYS FOR ME TO TELL YOU THAT IF YOU THROW ANYTHING THAT EVEN **LOOKS** LIKE IT MIGHT BE A BEAN-BALL, HE'S GOING TO COME OUT HERE AND POUND YOU RIGHT INTO THE GROUND!

I THINK THEY'RE BEGINNING TO GET TO ME...I NEED A NEW PITCH OR SOMETHING...WHAT DO YOU THINK I NEED, SCHROEDER?

A CONCRETE PILLBOX!

HI, ROY... WHO YOU WRITIN' TO?

I'M WRITING TO A LITTLE KID NAMED LINUS THAT I MET AT CAMP SEVERAL WEEKS AGO

IS HE CUTE? IF HE IS, TELL HIM YOUR VERY GOOD FRIEND, "PEPPERMINT" PATTY SAYS, "HELLO"

TELL HIM WHAT A REAL SWINGER I AM...

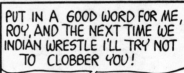

PUT IN A GOOD WORD FOR ME, ROY, AND THE NEXT TIME WE INDIAN WRESTLE I'LL TRY NOT TO CLOBBER YOU!

YOU SAY YOU MET THIS LINUS KID AT CAMP?

YES, AND THE YEAR BEFORE I MET A FRIEND OF HIS NAMED CHARLIE BROWN..

HE WAS A STRANGE ROUND-HEADED KID WHO NEVER TALKED ABOUT ANYTHING EXCEPT BASEBALL AND THIS AWFUL TEAM OF HIS THAT ALWAYS LOSES...

I LOVE BASEBALL! GET ON THE PHONE, QUICK! TELL HIM YOUR FRIEND, "PEPPERMINT" PATTY, HAS VOLUNTEERED TO HELP!

I REALLY LOVE BASEBALL! I'LL TAKE OVER THIS KID'S TEAM, AND SHOW HIM HOW TO **WIN**!!

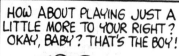

DEAR PEPPERMINT PATTY, I HOPE YOU HAD A NICE WALK HOME.

I JUST WANTED YOU TO KNOW THAT I APPRECIATED YOUR COMING CLEAR ACROSS TOWN TO HELP OUR TEAM.
SINCERELY,

" CHUCK "

EVERY NIGHT IT'S THE SAME..

I HAVE SUPPER IN MY RED DISH AND DRINKING WATER IN MY YELLOW DISH...

TONIGHT I THINK I'LL HAVE MY SUPPER IN THE YELLOW DISH AND MY DRINKING WATER IN THE RED DISH

LIFE IS TOO SHORT NOT TO LIVE IT UP A LITTLE !

AHEM!

OH, COME NOW! IF YOU'RE TRYING TO TELL ME IT'S SUPPERTIME, YOU'RE WAY OFF!

YOU'RE NOT EVEN **CLOSE**!

YOU MAY THINK IT'S SUPPERTIME, BUT IT ISN'T...

YOUR CLOCK MUST BE WRONG..

THAT'S HARD TO BELIEVE..

THIS IS GREAT FOR HIM..HE'LL SIT HERE ALL DAY AS LONG AS I SCRATCH HIS HEAD...

BUT WHAT DO I GET OUT OF IT? A HANDFUL OF TIRED FINGERS, THAT'S WHAT I GET OUT OF IT!

I STAND HERE SCRATCHING AND SCRATCHING AND SCRATCHING..I DO ALL THE WORK WHILE HE JUST SITS THERE..SOMETIMES I THINK HE TAKES ADVANTAGE OF ME

I'LL END UP GETTING TENDINITIS OR SOMETHING, AND HAVE TO GO TO A DOCTOR AND GET A SHOT... I COULD STAND HERE UNTIL BOTH MY ARMS FALL OFF FOR ALL HE CARES...GOOD GRIEF!

I'M THE SORT OF PERSON PEOPLE JUST NATURALLY TAKE ADVANTAGE OF...THAT'S THE TROUBLE WITH THIS WORLD...HALF THE PEOPLE ARE THE KIND WHO TAKE ADVANTAGE OF THE OTHER HALF!

WELL, I'M NOT GOING TO BE THE KIND WHO GETS TAKEN ADVANTAGE OF! I'M NOT GOING TO JUST STAND HERE AND SCRATCH HIS HEAD FOREVER

I REFUSE TO LET SOMEONE TAKE ADVANTAGE OF ME THIS WAY...I'M NOT GOING TO LET HIM DO IT... I MEAN, WHY SHOULD I?

I'M JUST THE SORT OF PERSON PEOPLE NATURALLY TAKE ADVANTAGE OF....

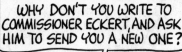

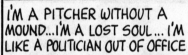

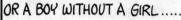

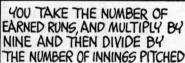

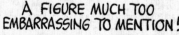

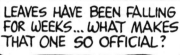

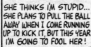

FANTASTIC!

HAVE YOU EVER KNOWN ANYONE WHO HAS THE GIFT OF PROPHECY?

JUST MYSELF

YOU?!

ABSOLUTELY! I CAN PREDICT WHAT ANY ADULT WILL ANSWER WHEN HE OR SHE IS ASKED A CERTAIN QUESTION..

IF YOU GO UP TO AN ADULT, AND SAY, "HOW COME WE HAVE A MOTHER'S DAY AND A FATHER'S DAY, BUT WE DON'T HAVE A CHILDREN'S DAY?" THAT ADULT WILL ALWAYS ANSWER, "EVERY DAY IS CHILDREN'S DAY!"

IT DOESN'T MATTER WHAT ADULT YOU ASK... YOU WILL ALWAYS GET THE SAME ANSWER..IT IS AN ABSOLUTE CERTAINTY!

I'LL TRY IT OUT ON GRANDMA..

GRANDMA, HOW COME WE HAVE A MOTHER'S DAY AND A FATHER'S DAY, BUT WE DON'T HAVE A CHILDREN'S DAY?

EVERY DAY IS CHILDREN'S DAY

THE GIFT OF PROPHECY!

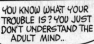

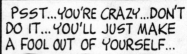

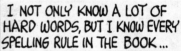

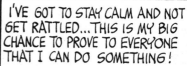

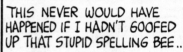

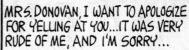

HELLO, SCHROEDER? GUESS WHAT... I CALLED TO TELL YOU I'VE BEEN LISTENING TO SOME BEETHOVEN MUSIC

I'VE ALSO BEEN READING HIS BIOGRAPHY...IT'S VERY INTERESTING.. SORT OF SAD, AND YET SORT OF INSPIRING...YOU KNOW WHAT I MEAN?

I HAVE A POST CARD, TOO, THAT I THINK YOU'D LIKE... AN UNCLE OF MINE SENT IT TO ME FROM BONN, GERMANY...THEY HAVE A MUSEUM THERE

I GUESS THAT'S WHERE BEETHOVEN WAS BORN, ISN'T IT? I'LL BET YOU'D ENJOY VISITING THERE.. MAYBE YOU'LL HAVE A CHANCE TO SOMEDAY...

ANYWAY, THAT'S WHY I CALLED BECAUSE I KNEW YOU'D BE INTERESTED, AND I JUST WANTED TO TELL YOU ABOUT THESE THINGS...

IT'S NOT PROPER FOR A GIRL TO CALL A BOY ON THE TELEPHONE

AAUGH!!

SCHULZ

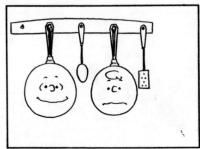

YOU KNOW WHAT?

I ALWAYS ENJOY SPECULATING ON WHAT OUR LIFE WOULD BE LIKE IF YOU AND I EVER GOT MARRIED, SCHROEDER...

I'LL BET WE'D HAVE A SON.. AND HE'D PROBABLY BE A GREAT MUSICIAN JUST LIKE YOU...

BUT I WONDER WHAT HE'D LOOK LIKE... I WONDER IF HE'D HAVE MY SENSITIVE EXPRESSION...

WHAT DO YOU THINK OUR SON WOULD LOOK LIKE?

WELL, PERHAPS.....BUT I'D LIKE TO THINK THAT HIS NOSE WOULDN'T BE QUITE THAT BIG...

IF DECEMBER TWELFTH IS HERE, CAN BEETHOVEN'S BIRTHDAY BE FAR AWAY?

GUESS WHAT...BEETHOVEN'S BIRTHDAY IS THIS WEEK, ISN'T IT? WELL, I'M GOING TO BAKE A CAKE, AND HAVE EVERYONE OVER! HOW ABOUT THAT?

I THINK SUCH AN EFFORT ON MY PART DESERVES A REWARD, DON'T YOU? LIKE MAYBE A LITTLE KISS...

I MEAN, AFTER ALL, SOMEONE LIKE YOURSELF WHO ADMIRES BEETHOVEN SO MUCH SHOULD BE WILLING TO REWARD A PERSON WHO WORKS HARD TO...

SMACK

AAUGH! I'VE BEEN KISSED BY A DOG!!

I'VE BEEN POISONED! GET SOME IODINE! GET SOME HOT WATER! GERMS! GERMS! GERMS!

HAPPY BEETHOVEN'S BIRTHDAY....THURSDAY!

WHAT'S THAT YOU'RE HOLDING?

IT'S A PENCIL...IT BELONGS TO THAT LITTLE RED-HAIRED GIRL... I'M GOING TO STAND HERE UNTIL SHE WALKS BY, AND THEN I'M GOING TO TELL HER HOW I FOUND IT...

I HATE TO SEE YOU GO TO ALL THAT TROUBLE, CHARLIE BROWN... WHY DON'T I JUST GIVE IT TO HER?

HEY! HERE'S YOUR STUPID PENCIL!!

WHY ARE YOU STANDING HERE, CHARLIE BROWN?

I'M WAITING FOR THAT LITTLE RED-HAIRED GIRL TO WALK BY..

I'M GOING TO SAY HELLO TO HER AND ASK HER HOW SHE'S ENJOYING HER SUMMER VACATION, AND JUST SORT OF TALK TO HER..YOU KNOW...

YOU'LL NEVER DO IT, CHARLIE BROWN...YOU'LL PANIC..

BESIDES THAT, SHE'S ALREADY WALKED BY!

HEY!

LOOK AT THAT, WILL YOU? WHAT'S THE MATTER?

THAT BIG KID JUST PUSHED DOWN THAT LITTLE RED-HAIRED GIRL! WHAT A BULLY!

SHE GOT UP....BUT, LOOK! HE'S GOING TO PUSH HER DOWN AGAIN!

OH, WHY AREN'T I TOUGH? WHY CAN'T I RUSH OVER THERE AND SAVE HER?

BECAUSE I'D GET SLAUGHTERED, THAT'S WHY! I'M NOT TOUGH... I'M NOT ANYTHING! I'M..

CRACK!

I'LL TAKE CARE OF HIM, CHARLIE BROWN!

CRACK!

YOU CAN RELAX, CHARLIE BROWN...HE WON'T BOTHER HER ANY MORE! THAT'S VERY COMFORTING... I'M THE FRIEND OF A HERO!

SCHULZ